SERIOUSLY SILLY JOKES

Why did the bus go mad?
It was driven to distraction!

Mother — "If you found a banknote on the street, would you keep it?"
Billy — "Of course not!"
Mother — "What a good boy! What would you do with it?"
Billy — "I'd spend it!"

Betty — "I've just come from the beauty salon!"
Barbara — "What a pity it was shut!"

Old gentleman — "And what does your father do, sonny?"
Little boy — "He drives other people's cars!"
Old gentleman — "So he's a chauffeur, is he?"
Little boy — "No – he's a car thief!"

Mother — "Jimmy, do you think you can tell me what was Napoleon's nationality?"
Jimmy — "Course I can!" (Corsican)

Molly — "How can I make a sculpture of myself out of this bit of clay?"
Mo — "Easy! Just take away all the bits that don't look like you!"

Two burglars broke into a theatre during a performance.
They were caught in the act!

Woman in newsagent's shop — "Do you keep stationery?"
Newsagent — "No, madam, I move about a bit, otherwise I get terribly stiff!"

Woman in dress shop — "Can I try on that pink dress in the window?"
Assistant — "Oh, no, ma'am, you'll have to use changing rooms!"

What did one plank say to the other one?
Are you coming to the board meeting?

Golfer (to caddie) — "What should I take for my next shot?"
Caddie — "Golf lessons!"

The politician finished addressing the crowd outside the shopping centre, but before he stepped down, he asked if there were any questions.

"Yes," said a small boy in the front of the crowd, "can I have the box you're standing on when you've finished with it?"

Bill — "I keep seeing spots before my eyes!"
Will — "Have you seen an optician?"
Bill — "No – just spots!"

Mum — "How's school?"
Son — "On the up!"
Mum — "On the up?"
Son — "Yes – sit up, stand up, own up, speak up and shut up!"

Little girl at dentist — "I wish we were born without teeth!"
Dentist — "We are!"

Maisie — "I can see right through you!"
Mo — "Oh, yeah? Then you can tell me what I had for breakfast today!"

Joe — "I can't put on my socks!"
Mum — "Why not?"
Joe — "Because the dog's just eaten them!"

Bill — "I fell in the river today!"
Will — "Wearing your smart new suit?"
Bill — "I'm afraid so – there was no time to change!"

Why did the writer write quickly?
Because his pen was running out!

Bobby — "Billy? Are you awake?"
Billy — "Not telling you!"

Few people know this, but when Anne Hathaway met William Shakespeare, it was love at first sight for both of them.

Their first date was very romantic, and Will walked Anne home, hand in hand, through the woods.

Halfway home, Anne stopped, dived into a thicket, and started to make a noise like an owl.

"Why hootest thou thus, my sweet?" asked Shakespeare.

"Because, my love," replied Anne, "a bard in the hand is worth 'two-hoo' in the bush!"

Old lady (to husband, who is 100 years old today) — "Look. The Queen's sent you a birthday message. Isn't that nice?"
Old man — "Huh! She never remembered before!"

When is a general like a ballet dancer?
When he is graceful in defeat!

Why is becoming a politician like being on a crowded bus?
Because you have to stand before you can get a seat!

Why did the doctor go to the bingo hall?
He wanted to make a house call!

Bob — "I used to be a child criminal!"
Batty — "And you changed your ways?"
Bob — "No – I grew up!"

Four monsters were out hunting for frogs for their evening soup.

Three of the monsters dribbled slime and goo constantly as they shuffled along, but the fourth waited until he came to a frog, then he would drop a couple of bits of slime on the frog – killing it, splitch, splotch, splash – just like that.

At the end of the hunt, the first three monsters had run dry, and had only five frogs each. The fourth monster had killed ten frogs and still had plenty of slime to spare. The moral of the story?

A splitch in time saves slime!

Midwife — "Well, Mr Jones, your wife has had a healthy baby!"
Mr Jones — "Is it a boy? I wanted a boy!"
Midwife — "Sorry, it's a girl!"
Mr Jones — "Never mind – that was my second choice!"

Fred — "People always phone my landline when I'm in the bath!"
Ted — "There's not much you can do about that!"
Fred — "Yes, there is – I've stopped taking baths!"

What's a snorkeller's favourite night out?
A dive-in movie!

Bob — "I could marry anyone I please!"
Bill — "So why are you still single?"
Bob — "I haven't pleased anyone yet!"

When is a lawyer like a tennis player?
When he's serving in court!

Maisie — "Where's my new lipstick?"
Mo — "It's on your mouth – right under your nose!"

Bill — "I'm off to the bottle bank!"
Will — "No need – I'll give you some of my bottles!"

Old lady — "I'm 85 and I've got a perfect set of teeth!"
Neighbour — "My, that's wonderful! How have you managed that?"
Old lady — "The dentist fitted them yesterday!"

How do you make an antidote?
Be very polite when she comes to visit!

The hairdresser lost his keys to the salon.
Luckily, he was able to change his own locks!

Why did Freddy become a fireman?
He wanted to join the jet set!

What did the farmer say when he turned up at the
publishers of the *Guinness Book of Records* with a giant
vegetable?
"Here's a turnip for the books!"

Billy — "Can I have a milkshake and two straws,
please?"
Waitress — "Are you going to share with your friend?"
Billy — "No – I just like to fill both sides of my mouth
at the same time!"

Molly — "My husband's a lighting engineer!"
Mo — "A bright young man?"
Molly — "No – a shady character!"

Scrawled on a toilet wall — "Don't just sit there – do
something!"

Why are camping enthusiasts good singers?
Because they always find the right pitch!

Did you hear about the spy who slept out in a gale?
His cover was blown!

How do you get to know a golfer?
Invite him for tee!

Did you hear about the photographer's near-death experience?
He saw his life flash before him!

Bill — "Do you like cartoons, Ted?"
Ted — "Oh, yes, I always listen to music when I go for a drive!"

What subject do keep-fit fanatics do best in at school?
Jog-raphy!

Mrs Jones — "Did you get fitted for your new trousers and jacket?"
Mr Jones — "No. They took my measurements and said I was unsuitable!"

Molly — "My mum's got a new dishwasher!"
Mo — "I wish my mum would get one too!"
Molly — "What's wrong with the one she's got?"
Mo — "I'm tired!"

Scrawled on a seaside wall — "School sucks."
Scrawled underneath — "So
     does
     qui
     ck
     sa
     n
     d!"

Mum — "So how was camp?"
Billy — "Great! But the food was terrible, I got bitten all over by mosquitoes, I fell out of a tree and hurt my arm, and the other kids were horrible!"
Mum — "So what was so great about it?"
Billy — "I didn't have to have a bath for a whole week!"

Kindly lady — "Can I help you, little girl?"
Little girl — "I can't reach this doorbell – can you ring it for me, please?"
Kindly lady — "There – is that it?"
Little girl — "Thanks – now, run for it!"

What happened when the undertaker took a one-man show on tour?
He got grave reviews!

What kind of car does a chemist drive?
A formula one!

What kind of car does a railway porter drive?
A station wagon!

What kind of vehicle does a refuse collector drive?
A pick-up truck!

What kind of car does a chicken farmer drive?
A hatchback!

What kind of car do anglers like best?
Hot-rods!

Did you hear about the man who always wore white when out walking at night so that the cars would see him?
He was knocked down by a snow-plough!

Bob — "I call my girlfriend 'Peach'!"
Bill — "Why – because her skin is soft?"
Bob — "No – because she has a heart of stone!"

Molly and Mo are eating apples.
Molly — "Watch out for maggots!"
Mo — "Why? The maggots can look after themselves!"

Why was the young pharaoh confused?
Because his daddy was a mummy!

Billy — "What are you putting that stuff on your face for, Mum?"
Mum — "To make me beautiful!"
Billy — "I'd take it back to the shop and ask for my money back, if I were you!"

Bill — "I'm going to get a water-bed!"
Will — "Oh, don't do that, Bill – you can't swim!"

Fred — "I've just been to America with Dave. It was great, but when we took our first look at the Grand Canyon, Dave's face dropped a mile!"
Ted — "Did he not like it?"
Fred — "No – he fell into it!"

Why are there no kings in the desert?
Because there is no rain (reign)!

Fred — "Does your dog bite?"
Ted — "No. He's got no teeth left. But don't go too close – he'll give you a nasty suck!"

"My father is a pilot in the air force. He distinguished himself in the war."

"My father is a fireman. He extinguished himself when his helmet caught fire!"

Annie — "So, do you think I should take up the violin as a hobby?"
Mo — "No, I think you should put it down as a favour!"

Fred — "I'm on a seafood diet!"
Ted — "What's that like, then?"
Fred — "Great – I see food, and I eat it!"

Annie — "It was test day at school today!"
Mum — "Really?"
Annie — "Yes. The teacher tested our English, and we tested her patience!"

Mum — "Davie, why are you crying?"
Davie — "I've got six peanuts stuck up my nose!"
Mum — "And why's your brother crying?"
Davie — "He wants the rest of his snack back!"

Bill — "Mr Dopey, I would like to ask for your daughter's hand in marriage."
Mr Dopey — "But what will I do with the rest of her?"
Bill — "What I meant was that I would like to take your daughter for my wife!"
Mr Dopey — "But why does your wife want her?"
Bill — "No – what I meant was that I would like to marry your daughter!"
Mr Dopey — "But you've got a wife already – you just told me!"

Bill — "What happened to you?"
Will — "I fell while I was out riding!"
Bill — "Horseback?"
Will — "I don't know – I haven't checked the stables yet!"

What is the best way to rise and shine?
Eat yeast and shoe polish!

What's the difference between a mirage and a mirror?
A mirage shows you what you long for and a mirror
shows what you fear!

Mum — "So, how was your second day at school, Jimmy?"
Jimmy — "Great – the teacher didn't shout at us once today!"
Mum — "You must have been very good, then!"
Jimmy — "No – after all her shouting yesterday, the teacher had lost her voice!"

Why did the man take a net to bed?
To catch forty winks!

Bill — "I love baked beans!"
Sue — "So do I!"
Bill — "Great – do you want to see my collection?"

Jim — "Mr Drone is a little bit dreary till you get to know him!"
Will — "And then?"
Jim — "And then you find out that he's a complete bore!"

Ted — "My girlfriend says I'm a great wit!"
Fred — "My girlfriend called me a great twit too!"

Molly — "My boyfriend said my legs were very striking!"
Maisie — "Did he?"
Molly — "Well, not exactly – he said they were like matchsticks!"

Jim — "I call my dog 'Treasure'!"
George — "Why is that?"
Jim — "Because the first time I took him home, my wife said 'Where did you dig that up?' "

Mum — "Quiet please, Johnny – your father can't read his paper!"
Johnny — "That's terrible – I learnt to read when I was five!"

Fred — "My brother's job really gets him down."
Ted — "What does he do?"
Fred — "He's a miner!"

Did you hear about the artist who became an actor?
He drew a large crowd at the theatre!

Old lady — "That's a very old teddy bear! What do you call him?"
Little girl — "Fred Bear!"

How do you hire a car?
Lift it with a crane!

Fred — "What's your sister like, Ted?"
Ted — "She's a swot!"
Fred — "Huh! Top in every subject, I suppose!"
Ted — "No, but she kills a lot of flies!"

What is the national drink of Australia?
Koka-Koala!

Mother (searching through old photographs) —
"Freddy, do you remember what I did with the prints
of Spain?"
Freddy — "I didn't even know you had met him!"

Interviewer — "And have you any children, Mrs Dobbs?"
Mrs Dobbs — "I had three girls – but now I've got two!"
Interviewer — "What happened to the third girl?"
Mrs Dobbs — "She grew up!"

Why is there a pile of letters at the end of the racecourse?
It's the finishing post!

Did you hear about the bad-tempered sailor?
He had a ship on his shoulder!

Maisie had earned a lot of money trick-or-treating. She
went to the shop to spend it. "If I had all that money,"
said the shopkeeper, "I would give it all to charity."
   "Righto," said Maisie, "I'll give it to you for these
sweets and then you can give it all to charity."

Why was the confectioner so proud of his children?
They were little sweeties!

Why did the boy take a clock and a bird out on
Hallowe'en?
Tick or tweet!

First man — "Does your baby cry much?"
Second man — "Cry? We call him the Prince of Wails!"

Fred — "I was woken by a terrible noise this morning!"
Ted — "What was it?"
Fred — "The crack of dawn!"

How did King Arthur get his men to dismount?
He waited for knightfall!

Bill — "I've got some money to spend and I'm going to
share it fifty-fifty with you!"
Will — "How much do we get?"
Bill — "I get fifty pounds and you get fifty pence!"

Billy — "I got you some perfume for your birthday,
Mum. It's called 'My Angel'."
Mum — "How nice! Why did they call it 'My Angel' I
wonder?"
Billy — "Probably because it smells to high heaven!"

Bill — "I've just found £20 – what should I do with it?"
Will — "Buy something nice with half and give me the
rest. The change will do me good!"

What did the executioner say to Charles I?
"You're history!"

"Help, help, my jacket's on fire!"
"That's a fine blazer you've got there, sir!"

First boy — "I've seen a man-eating tiger!"
Second boy — "So what? I've seen a man eating chicken!"

First boy — "I was named after my father."
Second boy — "So what do they call you?"
First boy — "Dad!"

First man — "My clients are always late for their appointments!"
Second man — "What do you do?"
First man — "I'm an undertaker!"

Maisie — "You haven't lost much weight – what happened to your four-week diet?"
Mo — "I finished it in two days!"

A little boy and his mother are going to the subway.
Little boy — "We can't go down there, Mum!"
Mum — "Why not?"
Little boy — "The sign says 'Dogs must be carried on the escalator', and we haven't got a dog!"

Where do company directors go when they have nothing to do?
The bored room!

Why did the bar on the high jump break?
An accident – nobody's vault!

What goes "peck-bang, peck-bang"?
Two chickens playing with balloons!

Why did the musician hold a shoe to his ear?
He was listening to sole music!

Sadie — "Our new baby fills the house with laughter and joy!"
Sid — "Our new baby fills the house with the smell of his nappies!"

What do sheep do straight after opening their Christmas presents?
They write their "thank-ewe" letters!

What does the sheepdog say when he guides the flock into the pen?
"After ewe!"

Which two months are dishonest?
FIBruary and JuLIE

Why was the painter hot?
He put on an extra coat!

Dad — "Johnny, how many times have I told you not to come down the stairs like that; it makes such a racket. Go upstairs again and come down quietly!"
Two minutes later. . .
Dad — "That's better. I didn't hear a thing that time!"
Johnny — "That's because I slid down the banister!"

Why did the snake fail his exams?
The examiner couldn't read his writhing!

What's the difference between a crossword solver and a man eating dessert?
One's a good puzzler and the other's a pud guzzler!

What's the difference between glue and sticky tape?
You've got me stuck there!

Boy genius — "There are sixty thousand ants in this anthill!"
Teacher — "How did you work that out?"
Boy genius — "Easy! I counted the legs and divided by six!"

Billy — "I'm glad I'm not a bird!"
Bobby — "Why?"
Billy — "Because I can't fly!"

Lifeguard — "Don't dive into the pool! There's no water in it!"
Man on diving board — "That's all right! I can't swim!"

Mike — "I'm not going to school today, Mum – the children hate me and the teachers are mean!"
Mike's mum — "You've got to go to school, son – you're the headmaster!"

Mo — "What have you got there, Molly?"
Molly — "It's a letter from a distant relative – my sister!"
Mo — "But your sister's not a distant relative!"
Molly — "Yes she is – she lives in Australia!"

What happened to the man who put his foot through a sieve?
He strained his ankle!

What did the daddy rabbit tell his friends when his wife had more babies?
"Fresh buns today!"

First boy — "I don't feel very well – I've got butterflies in my stomach!"
Second boy — "Huh! You're lucky! I've got a school dinner in mine!"

Billy — "I can't wind my watch!"
Bob — "Why not?"
Billy — "I lost it a week ago!"

Pandas live on bamboo shoots. What do polar bears live on?
Ice!

What did the skunk take to read on holiday?
A best-smeller!

Why was the sailor afraid of woodworm?
Because he had a wooden chest!

What is the latest letter in the alphabet?
"Y" – because it comes at the end of every day!

Teacher — "What do we do with crude oil?"
Billy — "We could teach it some manners, sir!"

"Dad, the car won't work. The engine's flooded."
"How do you know that, son?"
"Because I just reversed into the swimming pool!"

Fred — "I found six frogs today!"
Ted — "Where are you going to keep them?"
Fred — "In the bath!"
Ted — "But what will you do when you want to have a bath?"
Fred — "I'll blindfold them!"

Bill — "Is this plastic, or wood?"
Will — "It's wood!"
Bill — "Well, wooden you know it!"

Annie — "Have you seen *The Invisible Man*, Mo?"
Mo — "Don't be stupid!"

What musical instrument do lumberjacks play?
The TIMBER!-ine!

Angry man — "Come here! I'll teach you to throw stones at my greenhouse!"
Little boy — "Thanks, mister! I'm needing a few tips!"

What does a duck do when you tell it a joke?
It quacks a smile!

Maisie — "My friend's ambidextrous"
Mo — "I'd give my right hand to be like that!"

Fred asked his mum how old she was. Mum wouldn't tell him exactly how old she was, so Fred asked her if she was the same age as the mother and father of his best friend, Bill Hill. Mum said that she was.
  Next day, Fred had to write an essay on his mother.
  "My mother," he wrote, "is as old as the Hills. . ."

Why did the boy fall out of the plane?
He was annoying the other passengers and one of them told him to go outside and play!

Mum — "Tommy – you're bursting out of that jumper. We'll have to get you a new one!"
Tommy — "It must be the growing season for this family, Mum. Look at Dad – his head's bursting out of his hair!"

Scrawled on bike shed wall — "One good turn deserves another. . . keep it up and you'll get dizzy."

Why did the ghost go to the doctor?
To get something for his eerie-ache!

Bobby has been having dinner at his friend's house. A terrible storm comes. His friend's mum looks out at the wind and rain and says to Bobby "You can't go out in this terrible weather. You'd better just stay the night here."

"Righto," says Bobby. "I'll just run home and get my pyjamas and toothbrush!"

Betsy — "My dad's stronger than your dad!"
Annie — "Huh! That's rubbish. You know the Atlantic Ocean? My dad dug the hole!"
Betsy — "So what! You know the Dead Sea? My dad killed it!"

Santa Claus — "Rudolf says it's raining outside!"
Mrs Claus — "What makes you think he's right?"
Santa Claus — "Because Rudolf the Red knows rain, dear!"

A little boy arrives at a neighbour's house on Hallowe'en, with a sheet over his head.

"Are you a ghost?" asks the neighbour.

"No," says the little boy. "I'm just airing the bed linen for my mother!"

What's the difference between a person who can't mind his own business and a person who has just got out of the bath?
One's rude and nosey and the other's nude and rosy!

Why is painting such hot work?
Because two coats are necessary!

Annie and her mum are sitting on the bus, behind their next-door neighbour Mrs Brown. Annie whispers something in her mother's ear.

"Don't whisper, Annie," says her mother, "you know it's not polite. Now tell me what it is you wanted to say in a nice clear voice."

"Okay," says Annie, "I was just wanting to know why you think Mrs Brown is an old so-and-so!"

Mum — "Why are you listening to the radio and your mp3 player at the same time?"
Little Mo — "I like to keep both ears occupied!"

Why did the taxi driver give up his job?
Someone kept driving away his customers!

Billy (to sister) — "You're stupid and ugly!"
Dad — "That's quite enough! Say sorry to your sister!"
Billy — "Okay – I'm sorry that you're stupid and ugly!"

Billy falls down the stairs. "Ouch! ****** ****** *****" His language is shocking!

"Billy," says his mum, "you mustn't use language like that!"

"Shakespeare does," says Billy.

"Right," says his mum, "you're not playing with him any more!"

Mother ship to alien visiting earth — "So – is there intelligent life on the planet?"
Alien — "Yes, but I'm only here for a short while!"

**How do you stop a head cold from going to your chest?
Tie a knot in your neck!**

Ted — "I used to be so forgetful!"
Fred — "And are you any better now?"
Ted — "What were we talking about?"

Ted — "I've just bought a goat!"
Fred — "Where are you going to keep him?"
Ted — "Under the bed!"
Fred — "But what about the mess?"
Ted — "I'm sure he won't mind!"

Bill — "I bumped into an old friend the other day!"
Will — "Really? Was it good to see him?"
Bill — "I didn't see him – that's why I bumped into him!"

Wife — "Shall I put the kettle on, dear?"
Husband (not really listening) — "Whatever you like my love – you look wonderful in everything!"

What gets bigger by half when you turn it on its head?
The number 6!

Newspaper headline — "Basketweaving! Reed all about it!"

Will — "Are those two thin men very good friends?"
Bill — "No – they're just slight acquaintances!"

Auntie Doris — "My, my, you've grown another foot since I last saw you!"
Little boy — "I have not! I've got two feet, just as I always had!"

What is green and can jump a mile a minute?
A grasshopper with hiccups!

Ted — "Why are you swimming on your back?
Fred — "I've just eaten, and I don't want to swim on a full stomach!"

Ted — "Is it dangerous to swim on a full stomach?"
Fred — "Dunno – I always swim in water!"

What do you do with a haunted bicycle?
Take the spooks out of the wheels!

How did the gardener get lost?
He took the wrong root!

Two burglars in a music shop hear the sound of police sirens approaching. "Quick!" says one of them, "grab the lute and run!"

What did the headless ghost say when his friend gave him a comb?
"I'll never part with this!"

Can you drop an egg ten feet without breaking it?
Yes. Drop it from eleven feet up and it won't break for the first ten!

What did one lump of earth say to the other when they bumped into each other?
"Watch where you're going, you stupid clod!"

What do you call a vampire dentist?
An extractor fang!

What did the grumpy gardener say to his friend?
"Go away and leave me a-lawn!"

What do ghostly parrots say?
"Whoo-oo's a pretty boy, then!"

Which two letters spell rotten teeth?
D.K.!

How do gardeners get paid?
They get their celery once a month!

What do you do when you can't find the bath plug?
Look for the robber duck!

What did the burglar do in the supermarket?
He took what was on offer!

Did you hear about the robbery in the fishmonger's?
It was a smash-and-crab raid!

What do you call a millionaire who never washes?
Filthy rich!

Did you hear about the honest bowler?
He never did anything underhand!

Why are there no chairs in the prison concert hall?
Because on opening night, the audience took their
seats!

Why did the geologist take his girlfriend to the quarry?
Because he wanted to get a little boulder!

Why do robots never wash their hands?
They don't want to get rusty nails!

What do ghosts wear on their feet in wet weather?
Wail-ington boo-oots!

Owl — "To-whoo! To-whoo!"
Teacher — "To WHOM! To WHOM!"

Bill — "Our pet sheep's just like one of the family."
Will — "Yes, I can see the resemblance!"

What did the bus driver say to the man with the broken leg?
"Hop on!"

What is the difference between a bottle of perfume and a parcel?
One goes wherever it is sent, the other is scent wherever it goes!

What did the mole say when he met the worm?
"What in earth are you doing here?"

Where do ponies go when they're sick?
Horse-pital!

Why did the rodeo rider go to the doctor's?
Because he had bronco-itis!

What has fangs and says "Ten, nine, eight, seven. . .?"
Count Backula!

Will — "There are two caterpillars in camouflage outfits and tin helmets in the middle of this apple!"
Bill — "Don't worry – that's just the apple corps!"

How much do bakers get paid?
Lots of dough!

Gamekeeper — "Oi! you're not allowed to fish here!"
Fisherman — "I'm not fishing. I'm teaching this worm to bungee-jump!

A Spanish magician was performing at a party and told the audience he would disappear on the count of three. He said: "Uno...Dos..." and in a puff of smoke he was gone. He disappeared without a tres!

Bill — "Do you file your nails, Will?"
Will — "No, I just throw them away!"

First fish — "Percy the pike was caught today!"
Second fish — "What? After all those years? I bet he was fed up!"
First fish — "Fed up? He was gutted!"

Did you hear about the burglar who was arrested for breaking into a writer's home?
He got a long sentence!

Customer — "I cleaned my watch yesterday, and now it won't work!"
Jeweller — "What did you clean it with, sir?"
Customer — "Soap powder and water, of course!"
Jeweller — "Soap powder and water? No wonder it won't work now!"
Customer — "Oh, I don't think the washing was the problem, actually. It all went horribly wrong in the spin-cycle!"

Bill — "Where does your wife come from?"
Will — "Alaska!"
Bill — "Don't worry, I'll ask her myself!"

Man in fish shop — "Throw me that salmon, would you, please?"
Fishmonger — "Why?"
Man — "So I won't be lying when I tell my wife I caught it!"

What do you call a dentist in the army?
A drill sergeant!

Chef — "Can you lay five eggs over there by the cooker for me?"
Assistant — "What do you think I am? A chicken?"

What is the difference between a bus driver and a bad cold?
One knows the stops and the other stops the nose!

Did you hear about the judge who had his wig stolen from his head?
It was a hair-raising experience!

"My name is Mackintosh and I work in the clothing industry."
"My name is Hiram and I'm in the rental business."
"My name is Player and I'm a sportsman."
"My name is Idle and I don't do anything!"

"My name is Walker and I'm a driver."
"My name is Thrower and I'm a batsman."
"My name is Carpenter and I work in the demolition business."
"My name is Keen, and I'm just not interested!"

"My name is Frantz, and I come from Belgium."
"My name is Scott, and I'm American."
"My name is Isla and I come from the mainland."
"My name is Mappin and I'm lost!"

"My name is Rich and I haven't got a penny."
"My name is Rider and I haven't got a horse."
"My name is Carpenter and I haven't got a saw."
"My name is Smart and I haven't got a clue!"

"My name is Cross and I never lose my temper."
"My name is Watt and I never ask questions."
"My name is Cook and I never go near the kitchen."
"My name is Herd and I never listen!"

Where did the secret agent go shopping?
At the snooper-market!

Shop assistant — "I must say, sir, I'm surprised to see any customers on a day like this. It must be the wettest day in history!"
Customer — "I know, but my wife said I should splash out and buy a new suit!"

Why did the history teacher go to the grocer's shop?
He wanted some dates!

Bill — "Coming to the car boot sale?"
Will — "No thanks – I wear trainers when I'm driving!"

Customer in grocer's shop — "Do you have asparagus?"
Assistant — "No, we don't have any sparrows and my name's not Gus!"

Customer in hardware store — "Have you got two-inch nails?"
Assistant — "Yes, sir!"
Customer — "Scratch my back, then, will you?"

FOR SALE

Rubber gloves in handy packs!
Playing cards with eight aces – it's a great deal!
Second-hand buses – not to be missed!
Skittles – knock-down prices!
Coffins – a once-in-a-lifetime offer!
Cars for sale – Quick – they're going fast!
Unbeatable offer – drum with hole in it!

How do you choose a lawyer?
Ask for a free trial!

Fire sale! Red-hot deals!

"How did you get on at the garage sale?"
"They didn't have any garages I liked!"

A woman went into a shop, looking for a new bedroom
mirror. She caught sight of one that looked quite nice,
and went over for a closer inspection.
   "Do you like that one, madam?" asked the assistant.
   The woman looked into the mirror and frowned.
   "On reflection," she said, "no, I don't!"

An actor went into a shop looking for a new shirt.
They didn't have one that fitted him on the shelves,
but he saw one in the window that he thought might
be in his size, so he asked if he could try it on.
   "I'm sorry, sir," said the assistant, "but that shirt's
for display only."
   "Oh," said the actor, "and what play might that
be?"

Assistant — "Still here, sir?"
Robber — "Yes – just looting!"

**What kind of shop is full of unpleasant people?
The shoe-shop – you'll always find loafers and sneakers there!**

Customer — "Do your eggs come from a local farmer?"
Shop assistant — "No, sir – they all come from hens!"

**A shoplifter is heading out of the door of a department store when the alarm goes off. The store detective is there in a flash.
"May I look in that bag, sir?" he asks sternly.
"Of course," says the shoplifter, relieved. "Just don't ask what I have in my pockets, whatever you do!"**

Assistant — "Can I help you, sir?"
Robber — "No thanks – just lurking!"

**Customer — "This knife you sold me is blunt!"
Assistant — "Yes, sir, it's the new safety feature!"**

What do you call a clapped-out vacuum cleaner?
A poor old sucker!

**Customer — "Do you carry 20lb sacks of potatoes in this shop?"
Grocer — "No, sir. I get my assistant to do all the heavy lifting!"**

A man goes into an electrical goods store to buy a washing machine. "I want a nice quiet machine," he says. "The one I have at the moment is very noisy."

The assistant is very reassuring. "All our machines are very quiet," he says. "Why don't you take this one? It doesn't make a sound!"

The man buys the washing machine and has it delivered to his home, but two days later, he's back.

"That washing machine is just as noisy as my old one!" he complains. "You said it didn't make a sound!"

"It doesn't," says the shop assistant, "unless you switch it on!"

Did you hear that a ladder has been stolen from the hardware shop? The manager says that further steps will be taken.

Customer — "Could I have that loaf of raisin bread on the shelf over there?"
Assistant — "That's not raisin bread. We're just having a bit of a problem with flies at the moment!"

Shop assistant — "You're quite right, sir; you do need some new glasses!"
Customer — "You haven't tested my eyes yet! How do you know I need new glasses?"
Shop assistant — "Because this isn't the optician's – it's the fruit shop!"

Customer — "Are these chillis very hot?"
Grocer's assistant — "I don't think so, sir; they're sitting right by the doorway, and there's quite a draught!"

Customer — "Do you have any sweet potatoes?"
Grocer — "These ones are quite cute!"

Manager — "Did you count the takings?"
Assistant — "Yes, sir – they took half the contents of the shop!"

Customer — "Do you have crab's legs?"
Fishmonger — "I can assure you, sir; I walk forwards, just like you!"

What did one keyboard say to the other keyboard?
"Sorry, but you're not my type!"

Which computer game heroine wins prizes at dog shows?
Lara Crufts!

Which bit of a computer do astronauts like best?
The space bar!

Why did the sheep kick in the computer screen?
They were looking for the ram!

Why did Mr Dopey wear a helmet whenever he used his computer?
Because he was afraid it might crash!

How do archaeologists select their options from the computer screen?
They press the Dead Sea Scrollbar!

Why was the school computer keyboard upset?
Because it wanted to be a monitor!

Why could Mr Dopey not get his computer to work?
He couldn't find his keys!

Why did the elephant get rid of its computer?
It was afraid of the mouse!

Why couldn't the sailors play cards?
The captain was sitting on the deck!

What is a pirate's favourite letter?
Aaarrrr.

What do you call a monster with no neck?
The Lost Neck Monster.

What do you call a deer with no eyes?
No eye-deer!

Patient — "Doctor, doctor! Sometimes I think I'm a wigwam, and sometimes I think I'm a teepee. Please help! What is wrong with me?"
Doctor — "You're two tents!"

Patient — "Doctor, doctor! Please help me! I keep thinking I'm a dog!"
Doctor — "Well, hop up on the couch and lie down, and we can start from the beginning."
Patient — "Thank you doctor, but I'm not allowed on the couch!"

Did you hear about the two friends who met in a revolving door?
They are still going around together!

Why does the navy in Norway have bar codes on the side of the side of their ships?
So when they come back into port, they can Scandanavian!

Bill — "If you don't stop tapping away at that computer keyboard I think I'll go nuts!"
Will — "You've gone nuts already – I stopped half an hour ago!"

Why did the banana go the doctor?
Because he wasn't peeling very well!

Why wasn't there any food left after the monster party?
Because everyone was a goblin!

Why did the gardener plant a generator?
He thought he could grow a power plant!

Why do generators hum?
They don't know the words!

What did the electric light bulb say to the electric generator?
You spark up my life!

Why did the light bulbs go out?
Because they liked each other a lot!

Why is wind power popular?
Because it has a lot of fans!

What should we do about the crude oil?
Send it to school and teach it some manners!

Why is electricity so dangerous?
Because it doesn't know how to conduct itself!

One spaceman: "What did you think of that new café
on the moon?"
Second spaceman: "The milkshakes were good but it
had no atmosphere."

I tried to tell a chemistry joke at school the other day.
I got no reaction!

I was reading a book on anti-gravity.
I found it hard to put down!

What did the volcano say to his wife?
I lava you so much!

What do you call two dinosaurs that have been in an
accident?
Tyrannosaurus wrecks!

How does NASA organize a birthday party?
They planet!

Why do mushrooms look like umbrellas?
Because they grow in damp places!

Why are frogs so happy?
Because they can eat whatever bugs them!

How did Albert Einstein, inventor of the theory of
relativity, begin a story?
Once upon a space time...

Small boy — "Are you going to Egypt, sir?
Archaeologist — "Yes, little boy, I sphinx so!"

Never lend a geologist any money! You'll never get
your money back.
They think a short term loan is a million years!

What's the best thing about elevator jokes?
They work on so many levels!

How do you know your cat's been on your computer?
There are teeth marks in your mouse!

What do you get if you cross a computer with an
elephant?
A lot of memory!

What is the most thirst-quenching letter of the alphabet?
T!

What do you get if a cross a lifeguard with a computer?
A screensaver!

What did the big black spider do on the computer?
Make a website!

Why did Mr Dopey take his computer to the
optician's?
Because the screen was blinking!

How do cod type their e-mails?
With their fish fingers!

What do you get when you cross a cat with a parrot?
A carrot!

What do you get if you cross a lamb and a rocket?
A space sheep!

What kind of tree can give you a high five?
A palm tree!

What did the tree do when the bank closed?
It started its own branch!

What did the trees wear to the pool party in the forest?
Swimming trunks!

How do you get down from a tree?
You don't! Down comes from a duck, silly!

What is the most frustrating thing about being a tree?
Having so many limbs, and not being able to walk!

How many trees can you plant in an empty forest?
Just one. After that, it's not empty anymore!

What weighs more? A pound of leaves or a pound of
logs?
They both weigh about the same!

Where do you find a forest without trees, a road with
no cars and a town with no houses?
On a map!

What looks like half a spruce tree?
The other half of the spruce tree!

What happened when Amy Algae met Fergus Fungus?
They took a lichen to each other! But now their
friendship is on the rocks!

Two atoms are walking down the street.
One atom says to the other, "Hey! I think I lost an
electron!"
The other says: "Are you sure?"
"Yes, I'm positive!"

Why was the doctor's computer out of order?
Because it had a slipped disk!

Where did the jockey go on his holidays?
To Gallup in New Mexico!

Where do small dogs go for their holidays?
New Yorkie!

Where do baby birds go for their holidays?
Chickago!

Where do cats go on their holidays?
Miaowmi or Mew Zealand!

Where do dalmatians go on their holidays?
Spotland!

Where do mathematicians go on their holidays?
To see the Great Divide!

Why did the lawyer get upset on holiday?
Because he lost his case!

Where do shipbuilders go on holiday?
Hull!

Where do sheep go on their holidays?
Jersey!

Where do computers go on holiday?
IT-aly!

Where do sharks go on holiday?
Finland!

Where do criminals go on holiday?
Barred-cell-ona!

Where do sardines go on holiday?
Cannes!

Where do drivers go on holiday?
Rhodes!

Where do bakers go on holiday?
Flourida!

Where do financiers go on holiday?
The Costa Banka!

Where did the 100m sprint champion go on holiday?
Iran!

Where did the brown buffalo go on holiday?
Istanbul!

Where do shopping addicts go on holiday?
Mall-ta!

Where do turnips go on holiday?
Swede-n!

How did the carpenter reach his holiday destination?
He went by plane!

How did the cleaner reach her holiday destination?
She went in a hoovercraft!

**How did the chimneys reach their holiday destination?
They flue!**

How do bees travel on holiday?
By buzz!

**What do skunks ask for when they check into their
holiday hotel?
A room with a phew!**

Why did the postman go to Spain on holiday?
He didn't really want to go there, but he chose it as a last re-sort!

How do plumbers travel on holiday?
They go by drain!

How do elephants fly to India?
They go by jumbo jet!

Where do cats like to go on holiday?
To a-mews-ment parks!

Where do fishermen go on holiday?
Any plaice will do!

How did the bridesmaids get to go on the honeymoon?
They rode on the bride's train!

Why do sprinters always have a two-course meal?
Because they have to have a starter!

What did the policeman order for lunch?
Irish stew in the name of the law!

What did the weather man say when he opened his lunchbox?
"It's chilli again!"

What do actors like for breakfast?
A big role!

Why are golfers healthy eaters?
Because they like getting to the greens!

When do astronauts eat?
At launch time!

What would happen if you took the school bus home?
The police would make you take it back!

Mum — "How was your first day at school, Jimmy?"
Jimmy — "Rotten! The teacher told me to sit down and
be quiet for the present. . . and I didn't get one!"

Dad — "Well, Annie, how did you find school today?"
Annie — "Mum showed me the way!"

Mike — "My teacher's like rice pudding!"
Mum — "Aah! Is she sweet, and warm, and comforting?"
Mike — "No! She makes me sick!"

Pupil to English teacher — "I'll pass this spelling test, you mark my words!"
English teacher — "If I mark your words, you'll fail!"

How did the maths teacher get to school?
On his pi-cycle!

How did the science teacher get to school?
He came by test tube!

Why was the PE teacher sacked?
He wasn't fit for the job!

Why did the children run out of the cookery class?
Because the teacher said "Take one egg and beat it!"

First pupil — "I'm on playground litter duty today!"
Second pupil — "Things are picking up, then!"

First pupil — "Someone threw a stink bomb into the school toilets today!"
Second pupil — "So what does it smell like in there?"
First pupil — "A lot better!"

Why was the history teacher always out at night?
She had plenty of dates!

**Why did Susie put on lipstick and eyeshadow before
she went to school?**
**Because she had been absent and the teacher told her
she'd have to make up for lost time!**

Joe — "The teacher changed my English mark from a B
to a C today!"
Mum — "How do you feel about that?"
Joe — "Degraded!"

Why did the pupils have nothing to lean on in the English class?
Because all the tables were in the maths room!

Teacher — "Can anyone make a sentence for me, using the words 'defeat' and 'deduct'?"
Pupil — "Defeat of deduct are webbed, to help it swim!"

The teacher was angry because some pupils had scrawled rude messages all over the blackboard.
   "Would all those guilty of scrawling rubbish all over the blackboard please stand up!"
   There was silence for a while and then a little girl stood up.
   "Did you write something stupid on the blackboard?" asked the teacher.
   "No," said the little girl. "But I didn't want you to have to take all the blame!"

How do you get rid of a geography teacher?
Tell him he's history!

Mum (reading school report) — "What are all these F's for, Jimmy?"
Jimmy — "Fantastic!"

Johnny — "I think I might get an 'A' for effort in my report this year, Mum!"
Mum — "Why do you think that?"
Johnny — "The teacher said I was very trying!"

What did one school dinner-lady say to the other school dinner-lady?
"Only sixty slopping days left till Christmas!"

Dad — "What's all this, Billy? 'C' for Chemistry, 'D' for Drama, 'F' for French. . ."
Billy — "That's just the teacher showing that she knows her alphabet, Dad!"

Dad — "Jimmy, why are you crying? It's the first day of the summer holidays!"
Jimmy — "I know, Dad. And now I've only five weeks and six days until I'm back at school!"

Sam — "My teacher thinks I'm a miracle child!"
Mum — "Why is that?"
Sam — "She says it's a miracle I learn anything!"

Dad — "Bobby, why does your history exam have a great big zero at the bottom of the page?"
Bobby — "That's not a zero, Dad. The teacher ran out of stars, so she gave me a moon instead!"

Mum — "What's your new teacher like, Annie?"
Annie — "She's very nice, and she just loves me!"
Mum — "How do you know that?"
Annie — "Look at all the X's she put in my jotter!"

What kind of tree is best at maths?
Geometry!

Mum — "George, this note from the teacher says that all your homework sums were wrong!"
George — "I know; but don't tell Dad. He thought he'd done them quite well!"

How do you get full marks in a geometry exam?
It's easy, if you know all the angles!

Bobby — "Dad, can't you think of anything good to say about my report?"
Dad — "Well, son, with marks like that at least we know that you haven't been cheating!"

Dad — "What? It says on this paper you got only 26 for maths!"

Jimmy — "Oh, no, Dad, that's not my mark. That's the number of people in the class!"

What kind of tools are best at arithmetic?
Multipliers!

Dad — "What were your exam results like, son?"
Son — "Underwater, Dad."
Dad — "Underwater?"
Son — "Yep, well below C-level!"

Johnny — "I got 100 in an arithmetic test today, and I still didn't pass!"
Dad — "Why is that, son?"
Johnny — "Because the answer was 150!"

Why did the pencils get angry?
Because their box was rattled!

Little monster — "I hate my teacher!"
Mummy monster — "Well, put him to the side of your plate and eat up your vegetables, dear!"

Mother — "Off you go now, Johnny – oh, and here's some money for your lunch!"
Johnny — "Can't I have food like everybody else?"

What do French children say when they are given their school dinners?
Mercy!

Where do tiny insects go to learn to read and write?
Miniscule!

What was Camelot famous for?
Its knight life!

What did the leader of the Vikings say when his
longboat landed in Scotland?
"Right, men, take your Pict. . ."!

Why did Julius Caesar buy felt pens?
To Mark Anthony!

Why do dragons sleep all day?
Because they fight knights!

Which centurion in the Roman legion was best at
climbing?
IV!

Why did the lord of the manor arm his knights with
soap and buckets of water?
Because the peasants were revolting!

First Dragon — "Looks like they're eating beans for
supper!"
Second Dragon — "I'm staying in and reading my
book, then!"
First Dragon — "Why?"
Second Dragon — "I'm scared of windy knights!"

Why did King Arthur have a round table?
He wanted to invite a circle of friends to dinner!

What was the name of the first mouse to become emperor of Rome?
Julius Cheeser!

Why was the Norse god of war called Thor?
Becauth hith thaddle wathn't thoft enough!

Who was the most revolting emperor of Rome?
Disgustus!

What was the name of the first rodent to become a dictator in Italy?
Mouse-olini!

Who succeeded the first prime minister of Great Britain?
The second one!

Which king of England invented the apple box?
Alfred the Crate!

Why does history repeat itself?
Because no-one was listening the first time!

Who helped Noah design his boat?
An Arkitect!

Where did the explorers land when they reached America?
On their feet!

Notice on a knight's grave — "Here lies Sir Killalot, buried in his armour where he fell in battle. RUST IN PEACE."

Why were King Arthur's army tired?
They had too many late knights!

Which king was a champion rally-driver?
William the Cornerer!

Which king of England invented the fireplace?
Alfred the Grate!

What kind of trees do zombies like best?
Ceme-trees!

Newsflash — "Strange ghostly noises were heard on the roof of the multi-storey flats last night. Police say it was high spirits!"

How do you keep vampires out of your home?
Fang-shoo-i!

What do ghosts wear in the rain?
Ca-ghouls!

First monster — "You look like a million dollars!"
Second monster — "Do I?"
First monster — "Yes – all green and wrinkled!"

What did Dracula have for pudding?
Leeches and scream!

Did you hear about the ghost hospital?
It was full of surgical spirits!

Why do werewolves need a new coat each spring?
Because of the "were and tear" on the old one!

Did you hear about the one-eyed monster who took
up teaching?
He had a vacancy for a pupil!

What ghostly bird haunts the ocean shores by night?
The seaghoul!

What do you call an unmarried vampire?
A bat-chelor!

Why does the Abominable Snowman never wander
from the Himalayas?
Because there's snow place like home!

How can you tell when a vampire is old?
It gets long in the tooth!

Why did the scientist clone Dracula?
Someone demanded a re-count!

What did one vampire say to the other vampire at the tea table?
"Pass the jugular, please!"

Why do ghosts make good parents?
Because they go to all their babyscare classes!

What do you do if you find a ghost in your linen cupboard?
Give him some clean sheets!

What happens when you can't pay an exorcist?
You get re-possessed!

What do lorry drivers do on Hallowe'en?
They go truck-or-treating!

Can you trust a mummy to keep a secret?
Of course — mummies keep everything under wraps!

What do bad card players do on Hallowe'en?
They go trick-or-cheating!

Why did the mummy go on holiday?
It needed to unwind!

What do watchmakers do on Hallowe'en?
They go ticker-treating!

Why did the two three-eyed monsters fall out?
Because they didn't see eye-to-eye-to-eye!

What trails around the Himalayas at a speed of two miles a year?
The abominably slow-man!

What do ghosts do when they get in the car?
They fasten their sheet belts!

What do you call a cute vampire?
Draculaaah!

What kind of meal did they have at the ghosts' annual dance?
A boo-fet!

Why do ghosts wear sheets over their heads?
Because their clothes are in the overnight laundry!

How can you tell if a ghost's on the building site?
He's the one driving the screamroller!

What did the monster give his wife for their wedding
anniversary?
Shock-olates!

Mr Monster — "Can you hurry up with the dinner? I'm starving!"
Mrs Monster — "Give me a chance! I've only got two pairs of hands, you know!"

What is monstrous and frightening and makes your wishes come true?
A scary godmother!

Angler — "I haven't had a bite for hours!"
Vampire — "Perhaps I can help!"

What do you call a monster with good looks, a kind heart and a gentle nature?
A failure!

What do monsters like to drink?
Slime gore-dial!

Mummy monster — "Remember, I've got my eye on you!"
Little monster — "How can I forget, when you've stuck it on the end of my nose!"

First monster — "I'm going to be a teacher when I grow up!"
Second monster — "What makes you think you'll be good at it?"
First monster — "I've got eyes in the back of my head!"

Why was the little ghost fed up with school?
Because the teacher gave him a punishment exorcise!

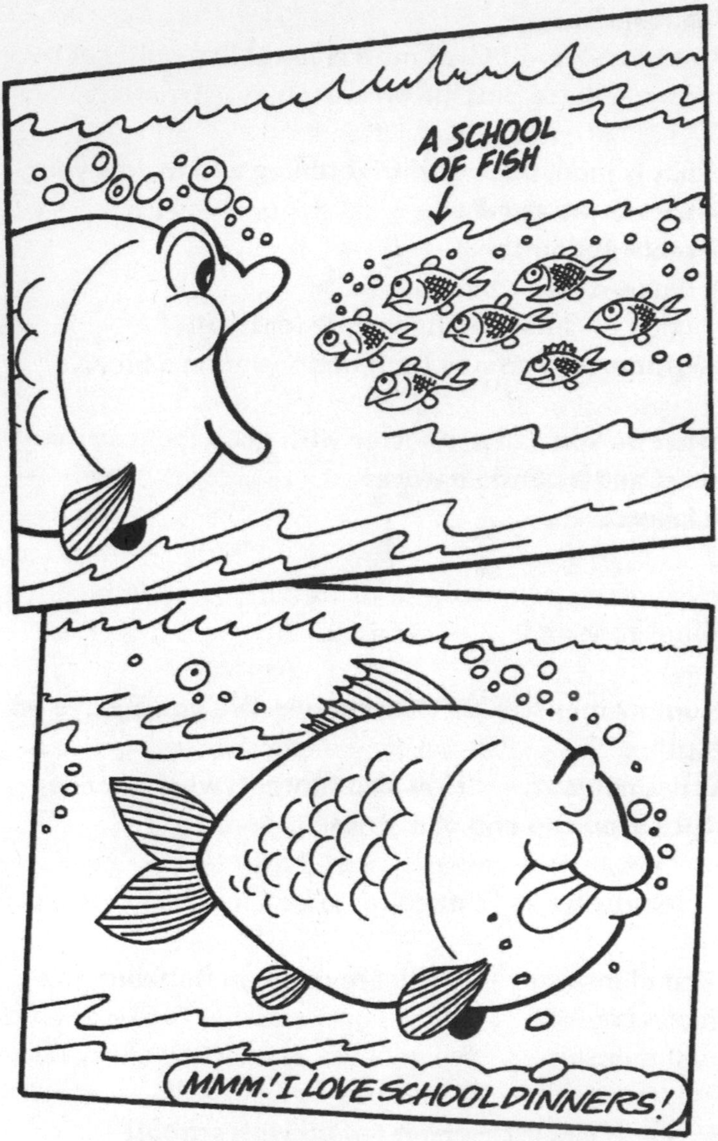
A SCHOOL OF FISH
MMM! I LOVE SCHOOL DINNERS!

What does a one-fanged vampire do?
Grin and bear it!

Why was the two-headed monster always short of money?
He had an extra mouth to feed!

What do you get if you cross a mummy with a vampire?
A blood-sucking bandage!

What do you call a one-eyed monster on a bicycle?
A cycle-ops!

Why did the cyclops teacher have an easy time of it?
He only had one pupil!

First monster — "Mrs Bloggs makes great stew!"
Second monster — "Delicious – but we'll miss her!"

Two aliens from outer space landed in the middle of London. They were walking along the street, when they came to a set of traffic lights. One of the aliens looked at the lights and then blushed.
    "What's the matter?" asked his friend.
    "She winked at me!" he said.

First monster — "I've just been on a crash diet!"
Second monster — "No wonder you look like a wreck!"

First monster — "Great new drink, this!"
Second monster — "Yes, gore-juice, isn't it?"

Jimmy — "Why are you looking so cross, Joe?"

Joe — "I won a prize for ugliest monster at the fancy dress party!"

Jimmy — "What's wrong with that?"

Joe — "I was just calling in to collect my little brother!"

What do you call a mummy that eats biscuits?
A crummy mummy!

What do you call a musical mummy?
A hummy mummy!

Why do zombies speak Latin?
Because Latin is a dead language!

What do you call a zombie who plays the drums?
A deadbeat!

Why did the ghost marry the skeleton?
Because he liked no-body better!

Why did Dracula's girlfriend leave him?
Because he was a pain in the neck!

Why did the monster refuse to eat the knight in armour?
He was sick of tinned food!

What did Dracula say to his girlfriend when she left him?
"That's right, off you go — find some other sucker!"

Why did the head haunt alone?
Because he couldn't find anybody he liked!

Little monster — "Mum! There's someone at the door with a really ugly face!"
Mummy monster — "Tell him I've already got one!"

What's shiny and scares monsters?
A mirror!

What did mummy monster say to little monster when he chased a human being round the garden?
"Stop playing with your food!"

Little monster is in trouble for being cheeky. His dad is giving him a row.
"And you can take that slime off your face right now!"

Why could the monster not sleep at night?
His brother kept telling him human stories!

First monster — "My, aren't you ugly!"
Second monster — "Why, thank you!"

A little boy is startled when a monster comes and sits beside him in the cinema.
"What are you doing here?" he asks.
"Well," says the monster, "I liked the book. . ."

Why was the werewolf's mother cross with him?
He didn't comb his face before he went to school!

Little monster — "Mummy, can I eat my pie with my fingers?"
Mummy monster — "No, dear, save your fingers for later!"

How did the monster come up with a great idea?
He put his heads together!

Newspaper advert — "Friendly monster for sale. House trained. Will eat anything. Loves children"!

Newspaper advert — "Friendly monster for sale. Will eat off your hand"!

Why was the invisible man upset?
He went away for two weeks and no-one noticed he was gone!

A boy is walking down the road with his pet monster when he is stopped by a policeman.
"You should take him to the zoo," says the policeman.
"I took him there yesterday," says the little boy. "We're going to the cinema today!"

Why was the fossil afraid?
Because it was petrified!

Why did Tolstoy's wife tell him to slow down?
Because he was Russian!

How do you make a Viennese whirl?
Play his favourite waltz!

How do you make bread rise?
Put it in the elevator!

How do you make an apple crumble?
Hit it with a sledgehammer!

What do actors do when they lose their temper?
They make a scene!

What vegetable makes us think of Christmas?
Peas on earth!

Why did the hermit eat a box of grass seed?
He wanted to be a-lawn!

Why is a panda dangerous?
Because it eats bamboo leaves and shoots!

Why did the boy take hay to bed?
To feed his nightmare!

Where was Solomon's Temple?
At the side of his head!

What did the old lady say when she crashed her mini into a flashy big car?
"So that's the way the Mercedes Benz!"

What kind of car does a railway porter drive?
A station wagon!

What kind of vehicle does a refuse collector drive?
A pick-up truck!

What kind of car does a chicken farmer drive?
A hatchback!

What kind of car do anglers like best?
Hot-rods!

What kind of car does a skeleton drive?
A boneshaker!

What kind of car does a Wild West bartender drive?
A saloon!

What do you get if you cross a polar bear with a harp?
A bear-faced lyre!

What kind of car does a shepherd drive?
A lamb-drover!

What kind of car does a sewer worker drive?
A poo-geot!

What kind of car does a lemon-grower drive?
A citron!

What kind of vehicle does an aquarium owner drive?
A tank!

What kind of car do dolphins like?
A multi-porpoise vehicle!

What kind of car do whales like?
Four-whale drive!

What kind of car does an electrician drive?
A voltswagon!

What kind of car does an orthopedic surgeon drive?
A limb-ousine!

What kind of cars do bakers drive?
Rolls!
What kind of car does a nurse drive?
A jag-you-aargh!

Why did the minister take his car to church?
He was putting it in for a service!

Bill — "Of course, the Vikings didn't have cars. They
had longships!"
Will — "How were they powered?"
Bill — "Twelve men sat on each side of the ship and
rowed."
Will — "Ah! Twenty-four Norse power, eh!"

What are the hottest letters of the alphabet?
BBQ!

What's a film about hard potatoes?
Mashin' Impossible!

What's a film about a dishonest monarch?
The Lyin' King!

What's a film about an elf on a desert island?
Gnome Alone!

"I'm giving my mother a pet canary!"
"That's nice — she deserves a tweet!"

**Did you hear about the two octopuses who fell in love?
They went everywhere arm in arm in arm in arm in
arm in arm in arm in arm!**

How did the florist meet her boyfriend?
She made an arrangement with him!

**Why did the astronaut split up with his girlfriend?
He needed more space!**

Why did the gardener's girlfriend fall in love with him?
He grew on her!

**Why did the soldier's girlfriend fall in love with him?
He gave her lots of attention!**

What happens when two swimmers get married?
They take the plunge!

**Why did the fisherman fall in love?
He was hooked!**

How did the balloon seller ask his girlfriend to marry him?
He popped the question!

**Was the musician's girlfriend excited when he asked her out?
No – she was perfectly composed!**

What happened when the two cooks announced their engagement?
There was quite a stir!

**Why did the fisherman's girlfriend agree to marry him?
He was quite a catch!**

Why did the waiter say no when his girlfriend proposed?
Because he had reservations!

Why did the grandfather clock fall in love with the grandmother clock?
Because she was striking!

What did one sand-dune say to the other sand-dune?
"I will never desert you!"

What happens when tennis players get together for a party?
They make a terrible racket!

Did you hear about the undertakers' party?
It was a g-rave!

What kind of party do dollies have?
A Barbie-Q!

Why are parties in the jungle so smart?
The animals all wear tails!

Do librarians ever have parties?
Yes, but they're always QUIET affairs!

Did Harry the Horse have many guests at his party?
Yes — he invited all the neigh-bours!

Did you hear about the underwater nightclub?
It's a bit of a dive!

What kind of parties do mathematicians prefer?
Square dances!

Why did Broken-leg Bill get all dressed up on Saturday night?
He was going to the hop!

How do train drivers have a good time?
They go line-dancing!

Why are police officers good dancers?
Because they keep to the beat!

What is a banker's favourite party game?
Musical Shares!

What do tennis players drink at parties?
Deuce!

How did the sentry celebrate his birthday?
He held a guardin' party!

What kind of music do gardeners like?
Mow-town!

What kind of music do mechanics like?
Garage!

Do astronauts have parties?
Yes — they invite their friends to launch from time to time!

Did you hear about the anaesthetist's party?
It was a gas!

What do archaeologists drink at parties?
Carbon-dated water!

There was a terrible fight at the actors' party —
They all wanted the bread role!

What is a postman's favourite party game?
Pass the parcel!

What is a fisherman's favourite party game?
Sardines!

What is a secret agent's favourite game?
I-spy!

What is an engineer's favourite card game?
Bridge!

What game do ghosts enjoy?
Hide-and-shriek!

What did the shipwrecked sailor do for his mother's
birthday dinner?
He washed up afterwards!

What did the philosopher want for his birthday?
Anything – it's the thought that counts, after all!

Bill — "I don't mind what I get for my birthday as long as it's wrapped up in paper, and given with real warmth!"
Will — "Here you are then — fish and chips!"

What do you call a man with a stamp on his head?
Frank!

What do you call a girl with a fish on her head?
Annette!

What do you call a woman with a target on her head?
Miss!

What do you call a man with a raincoat on his head?
Mac!

What do you call a man with a bill on his head?
Owen!

What do you call a man with a kilt on his head?
Scott!

What do you call a man with a baby's bed on his head?
Scot!

What do you call a man with a boat on his head?
Bob!

What do you call a woman with a snail on her head?
Shelley!

What do you call a man with a loudspeaker on his head?
Mike!

What do you call a man with the contents of the vacuum cleaner on his head?
Dusty!

What do you call a man with nothing on his head?
Just Ed!

What do you call a man with a haystack on his head?
Rick!

What do you call a man with a petrol pump on his head?
Phil!

What do you call a woman with a small car on her head?
Minnie!

What do you call a woman with a horse on her head?
Winnie!

What do you call a man with a legal document on his head?
Will!

What do you call a man with a crane on his head?
Derek!

What do you call a woman with a chimney on her head?
Ruth!

What do you call a woman with a radiator on her head?
Anita!

What do you call a man with a car number plate on his head?
Reg!

What do you call a man with a wig on his head?
Aaron!

What do you call a man with a map on his head?
Miles!

What do you call a woman with a spring on her head?
April!

What do you call a man with a purple and blue bump on his head?
Bruce!

What do you call a man with a spade in his head?
Doug!

What do you call a man with a spade in his head who has lost his dog?
Douglas!

What do you call a woman with a Christmas tree on her head?
Carol!

What do you call a woman with red berries on her head?
Holly!

What do you call a man with a seagull on his head?
Cliff!

What do you call a man with a paper bag on his head?
Russell!

What do you call a woman with two lavatories on her head?
Lulu!

What do you call a man with a plank on his head?
Edward!

What do you call a man with a car on his head?
Jack!

What do you call a man painted scarlet all down one side?
Alfred!

What do you call a woman with a tap on her head?
Flo!

**How can you recognise Mr Dopey at the car wash?
He's the one on the motorbike!**

A man was out riding his new motorbike while his
wife watched from the window.

The first time he passed, he called out, "Look, no
hands!"

Then there was a loud crash.

After a moment or two, the man rode past the
window again.

This time he called out to his wife, "Look, no
teeth!"

What flower should never be placed near balloons?
The poppy!

Billy — "I failed my trumpet exam!"
Mum — "Why?"
Billy — "Don't know – I just blew it!"

It's gone forever!
What?
Yesterday!

How do comedians entertain their friends?
They hold a tee-hee party!

What kind of food do photographers prefer?
Cheese!

What do geologists do in their spare time?
They go to rock concerts!

When do plankton have family get-togethers?
Every once in a whale!

What do bakers wear on their days off?
Loafers!

What did the lawyer name her children?
Will and Sue!

Why was the baker fed up with his children?
They wouldn't rise in the mornings!

If a man was born in France to an Italian mother and a German father, lived all his life in England and died in the USA, what would that make him?
Dead!

What do you call an octopus with nine legs?
An octoplus!

What flies around the seashore with wooden planks attached to its feet?
A ski-gull!

What kind of cooker does a famous person have?
One with a fan-assisted oven!

Jim — "And how did you get on at the talent show?"
Joe — "The audience was helpless with laughter!"
Jim — "So you did a comic routine?"
Joe — "No!"

What do patriotic insects sing?
The Gnat-ional Ant-them!

What is the difference between a good golfer and a bad golfer?
One has to replace the turf. The other has to returf the place!

What part of a football stadium is never the same?
The changing rooms!

Did you hear about Mr Dopey's water-skiing holiday? He came home because he couldn't find a lake with a slope!

Diver — "My last dive stunned the crowd!"
Friend — "It must have been spectacular!"
Diver — "Not exactly — my swimming trunks came off!"

Why is there a cat on the photocopying machine? He's the copy-cat!

Why did the cricketer go to the doctor?
Because he had the runs!

Why does it take a golfer so long to iron his clothes? Because he uses five-irons!

What athletic event are real cool dudes best at?
The hip-tathlon!

What athletic event are writers best at? The pen-tathlon!

What athletic event are rugby players best at?
The try-athlon!

New edition published 2017 by Geddes & Grosset, an imprint
of The Gresham Publishing Company Ltd, Academy Park,
Building 4000, Gower Street, Glasgow, G51 1PR, Scotland

www.geddesandgrosset.com
info@geddesandgrosset.co.uk
facebook/pages/geddesandgrosset

ISBN 978 1 84205 674 5

Printed and bound in the EU